ISBN 978-0-9797042-6-0
Library of Congress Control Number: 2011925210

Created by: Khane-Faygl Turtletaub, Ph.D.
Distributed by and available for purchase from:
Mame-Loshn Productions
8914 Central Park Avenue
Evanston, Illinois 60203
(847) 675-3335
www.mameloshnproductions.com

With support by and also available from:
Walder Education Pavilion
8150 McCormick Boulevard
Skokie, IL 60076
(847) 674-0800
www.waldereducation.com

Manufactured in the United States of America by:
ImagiCom Media Graphics, Inc.
8770 West Bryn Mawr Avenue
Chicago, IL 60631
(773) 714-4939
www.imagicommedia.com

Yiddish Transliteration Pronunciation Guide:

"a" pronounced as "a" as in "father"

"e" pronounced as "e" in "red"

"i" pronounced as "i" in did

"o" is between "aw" in "dawn" and "o" in "done"

"u" pronounced as "oo" in "took"

"ay" pronounced as "ay" in "May"

"ey" pronounced as "ey" in "they"

"kh" pronounced as "ch" in "Bach"

"tsh" pronounced as "ch" in "such"

"zh" pronounced as "s" in "treasure"

Yiddish Songs
For Children

by Dr. Khane-Faygl Turtletaub

Includes English, Yiddish, Yiddish Transliteration
and Musical Score....Plus All Recorded Music on CD

Mame-Loshn Productions
Chicago, Illinois

Acknowledgements

With thanks to **HaShem**, after a long time in the making, we have completed this original work of 14 Yiddish children's songs with accompanying illustrations and lyrics in Yiddish, English and transliteration.

This project could not have been accomplished without the dedication and commitment of **Dr. Yosef and Shira Malka Walder.** To both of these very special people I offer my heartfelt thanks for your friendship and support during the last few years. Your deep desire to make these songs available to children and families in Jewish communities throughout the world took this project from dream to reality.

To the extremely talented musical genius, **Leib Yaakov Rigler** of Jerusalem: I bless the day you agreed to arrange the music and record the sound track of these songs with some of the finest musicians in Israel. You have made these songs "sing" in a way no one else could have done.

To the **Hill Brothers of Eretz Yisroel**: your beautiful voices full of *yidishn kheyn* can now be shared with so many of your brothers and sisters everywhere.

I also want to express my gratitude to the late **Arnold Miller** for his sage musical advice, and to **Raisa Bekerman**, a wonderful musician, who livened up the melody of *"Tsedaka"* from the one I had.

My deepest gratitude to **Liz Elsby** for her charming illustrations, and to my graphic designer **Devorah Haggar**, for bringing it all together and giving it life.

Thanks to my dear husband, **Shepsl**, for his sage advice and encouragement. And of course, I cannot forget to thank **my four children**, who were the inspiration for these songs. Without you these songs would not exist.

— Khane-Faygl Turtletaub

Table of Contents

2

Yiddish

It's nice when your mother speaks Yiddish.
It's nice when your father speaks Yiddish.
It's nice when your aunt speaks Yiddish.
Yiddish should be spoken in the home!

It's nice when your grandfather speaks Yiddish.
It's nice when your grandmother speaks Yiddish.
It's nice when your sister speaks Yiddish.
Yiddish should be spoken in the home!

Refrain

Yiddish...What a language!
It's delicious.
Yiddish is beautiful to speak.
It's charming.
Yiddish, Yiddish, Yiddish,
Yiddish, Yiddish, Yiddish,
Yiddish should be spoken in the home!

It's nice when your uncle speaks Yiddish.
It's nice when your brother speaks Yiddish.
It's nice when everyone speaks Yiddish.
Yiddish should be spoken in the home!

It's a beautiful language!

יִידִיש

ס'איז שיין ווען די מאַמע רעדט יִידיש.
ס'איז שיין ווען דער טאַטע רעדט יִידיש.
ס'איז שיין ווען די מומע רעדט יִידיש.
יִידיש זאָל מען רעדן אין דער היים.

ס'איז שיין ווען דער זיידע רעדט יִידיש.
ס'איז שיין ווען די באָבע רעדט יִידיש.
ס'איז שיין ווען די שוועסטער רעדט יִידיש.
יִידיש זאָל מען רעדן אין דער היים.

רעפֿרען

יִידיש, סאַראַ שפּראַך.
ס'איז אַזוי געשמאַק.
יִידיש רעדט זיך שיין.
ס'איז דאָך מלא-חן.
יִידיש, יִידיש, יִידיש,
יִידיש, יִידיש, יִידיש.
יִידיש זאָל מען רעדן אין דער היים.

ס'איז שיין ווען דער פֿעטער רעדט יִידיש.
ס'איז שיין ווען דער ברודער רעדט יִידיש.
ס'איז שיין ווען אַלע רעדן יִידיש.
יִידיש זאָל מען רעדן אין דער היים.

ס'איז אַ שיינע שפּראַך!

Yidish

ייִדיש

ייִדיש

S'iz sheyn, ven di mame redt yidish.
S'iz sheyn, ven der tate redt yidish.
S'iz sheyn, ven di mume redt yidish.
Yidish zol men redn in der heym!

S'iz sheyn, ven der zeyde redt yidish.
S'iz sheyn, ven di bobe redt yidish.
S'iz sheyn, ven di shvester redt yidish.
Yidish zol men redn in der heym!

Refren

Yidish—sara shprakh.
S'iz azoy geshmak.
Yidish redt zikh sheyn.
S'iz dokh mole-kheyn.
Yidish, yidish, yidish,
Yidish, yidish, yidish,
Yidish zol men redn in der heym!

S'iz sheyn, ven der feter redt yidish.
S'iz sheyn, ven der bruder redt yidish.
S'iz sheyn, ven ale redn yidish.
Yidish zol men redn in der heym!

S'iz a sheyne shprakh!

ייִדיש

ייִדיש

Yiddish

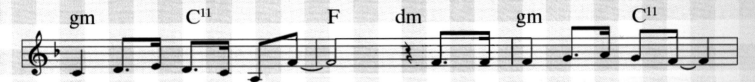

Thank You

I offer thanks to You G-d for Your goodness,
Living, eternal King.
You restore my soul to me every day.
Your faithfulness makes me happy.

Yiddish

מודה אני

אִיךְ דאַנק דִיר ג־ט פֿאַר דײַן גנאָד,

לעבעדיקן אייביקן מלך.

דו קערסט מיר די נשמה אום אַלע טאָג.

דײַן געטרײַשאַפֿט מאַכט מיך פֿרײלעך.

Transliteration

Moyde Ani

Ikh dank dir G-t far dayn gnod,
Lebedikn eybikn meylekh.
Du kerst mir di neshome um ale tog.
Dayn getrayshaft makht mikh freylekh.

Moyde Ani

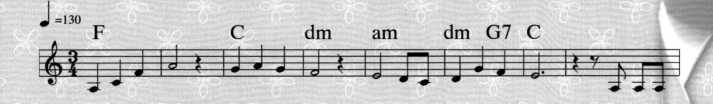

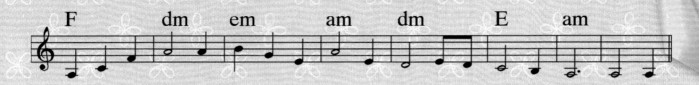

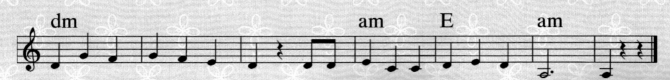

Whatever One Does

When Beyla the baker
Kneads her dough,
She kneads it with all her heart.

When Tuvya the ink maker
Makes his ink,
His black ink is really black.

Refrain

Whatever one does
One should do well,
If not then just for spite
It doesn't come out right.

When Mendl the teacher teaches
in school,
His class is the best one.
When Gershon, a good boy,
Sits down at the table,
He eats whatever he's given.

Refrain

When Moshe the musician
Plays his violin
He's not thinking of pancakes.
He's thinking of the notes
And the music
And how the bow produces
these [sounds].

Refrain

When one stands to pray
And when one says a blessing,
One should really concentrate,
Or it's not worth doing at all.

Refrain

וואָס מע טוט

וועו ביילע די בעקערקע
קנייט איר טייגל,
קנייט זי מיטן גאַנצן האַרץ.

ווען טוביה דער טינטמאַכער
מאַכט זײַן טינט,
מאַכט ער שוואַרץ--איז שוואַרץ.

רעפֿרעו:

וואָס מע טוט
דאַרף מען טאָן גוט.
אַז נישט, ווי אויף צו להכעיס
טויג עס אויף כפרות

ווען מענדל מלמד לערנט אין חדר
איז זײַן קלאַס דער בעסטער.
ווען גרשון, אַ גוט יינגל
זעצט זיך צום טיש
וואָס מע גיט אים עסט ער.

רעפֿרעו:

ווען משה דער מוזיקאַנט
שפילט זײַן פֿידל,
טראַכט ער נישט פֿון לאַטקעס.
ער טראַכט פֿון די נאָטן און דער מוזיק
און ווי דער סמיטשיק מאַכט עס.

רעפֿרעו:

ווען מע שטעלט זיך דאַוונען
און ווען מע מאַכט אַ ברכה
דאַרף מען מאַכן מיט כוונה.
אויב נישט טויג עס אויף כפרות.

רעפֿרעו:

Vos Me Tut

Ven Beyle di bekerke
Kneyt ir teygl,
Kneyt zi mitn gantsn harts.

Ven Tuvye der tintmakher
Makht zayn tint,
Makht er shvarts
--iz shvarts.

Refren

> Vos me tut
> Darf men tun gut.
> Az nisht, vi af tselokhes
> Toyg es af kapores.

Ven Mendl melamed
  lernt in kheyder
Iz zayn klas der bester.
Ven Gershon, a gut yingl,
Zets zikh tsum tish
Vos me git im est er.

Refren:

Ven Moyshe der muzikant
Shpilt zayn fidl
Trakht er nisht fun latkes.
Er trakht fun di notn
Un der muzik
Un vi der smitshik makht es.

Refren:

Ven me shtelt zikh davenen
Un ven me makht a brokhe
Darf men makhn mit kavone,
Oyb nisht toyg es af kapores.

Refren:

Vos Me Tut

I Am a Jew

Refrain

I am a Jew. I am a Jew.
I am, I am a Jew.
I am a Jew. I am a Jew.
I am, I am a Jew..

What does a Jew do? What does a Jew do?
What does, what does a Jew do?
What does a Jew do? What does a Jew do?
What does, what does a Jew do?

A Jew does good deeds, good deeds every day.
A Jew says blessings, blessings every day.
A Jew prays, prays every day.
That's what a Jew does.

Refrain:

What does a Jew wear? What does a Jew wear?
What does, what does a Jew wear?
What does a Jew wear? What does a Jew wear?
What does, what does a Jew wear?

A Jew wears ritual fringes, fringes every day.
A Jew wears a skullcap, a skullcap every day.
A Jew has G-d in his heart every day.
That's what a Jew wears.

Refrain:

"Little boys wear ritual fringes
    and yarmulkes.
What do little Jewish girls do?"

They do good deeds, good deeds every day.
They say blessings, blessings every day.
They have G-d in their hearts every day.
That's what they do.

Refrain:

איך בין אַ ייִד

איך בין אַ ייִד, איך בין אַ ייִד.

איך בין, איך בין אַ ייִד.

איך בין אַ ייִד, איך בין אַ ייִד.

איך בין, איך בין אַ ייִד.

וואָס טוט אַ ייִד? וואָס טוט אַ ייִד?

וואָס טוט, וואָס טוט אַ ייִד?

וואָס טוט אַ ייִד? וואָס טוט אַ ייִד?

וואָס טוט, וואָס טוט אַ ייִד?

אַ ייִד טוט מיצוות, מיצוות אַלע טאָג.

אַ ייִד מאַכט ברוכות, ברוכות אַלע טאָג.

אַ ייִד דאַוונט, דאַוונט אַלע טאָג.

דאָס טוט אַ ייִד.

רעפֿרען:

וואָס טראָגט אַ ייִד? וואָס טראָגט אַ ייִד?

וואָס טראָגט, וואָס טראָגט אַ ייִד?

וואָס טראָגט אַ ייִד? וואָס טראָגט אַ ייִד?

וואָס טראָגט, וואָס טראָגט אַ ייִד?

אַ ייִד טראָגט ציצית, ציצית אַלע טאָג.

אַ ייִד טראָגט אַ קאפל, אַ קאפל אַלע טאָג.

אַ ייִד טראָגט ג־ט אין האַרצן אַלע טאָג.

דאָס טראָגט אַ ייִד.

רעפֿרען:

ייִנגעלעך טראָגן ציצית און קאפלעך.

וואָס טוען ייִדישע מיידעלעך?

זיי טוען מיצוות, מיצוות אַלע טאָג.

זיי מאַכן ברכות, ברכות אַלע טאָג.

זיי טראָגן ג־ט אין האַרצן אַלע טאָג.

דאָס טוען זיי.

רעפֿרען:

Ikh Bin a Yid

Refren

Ikh bin a yid. Ikh bin a yid.
Ikh bin, ikh bin a yid.
Ikh bin a yid. Ikh bin a yid.
Ikh bin, ikh bin a yid.

Vos tut a yid? Vos tut a yid?
Vos tut, vos tut a yid?
Vos tut a yid? Vos tut a yid?
Vos tut, vos tut a yid?

A yid tut mitsves, mitsves ale tog.
A yid makht brokhes, brokhes ale tog.
A yid davent, davent ale tog.
Dos tut a yid.

Refren:

Vos trogt a yid? Vos trogt a yid?
Vos trogt, vos trogt a yid?
Vos trogt a yid? Vos trogt a yid?
Vos trogt, vos trogt a yid?

A yid trogt tsitses, tsitses ale tog.
A yid trogt a kapl, a kapl ale tog.
A yid trogt G-t in hartsn ale tog.
Dos trogt a yid.

Refren:

"Yingelekh trogn tsitses un kaplekh.
Vos tuen yidishe meydelekh?

Zey tuen mitsves, mitsves ale tog.
Zey makhn brokhes, brokhes ale tog.
Zey trogn G-t in hartsn ale tog.
Dos tuen zey.

Refren:

I Am a Jew

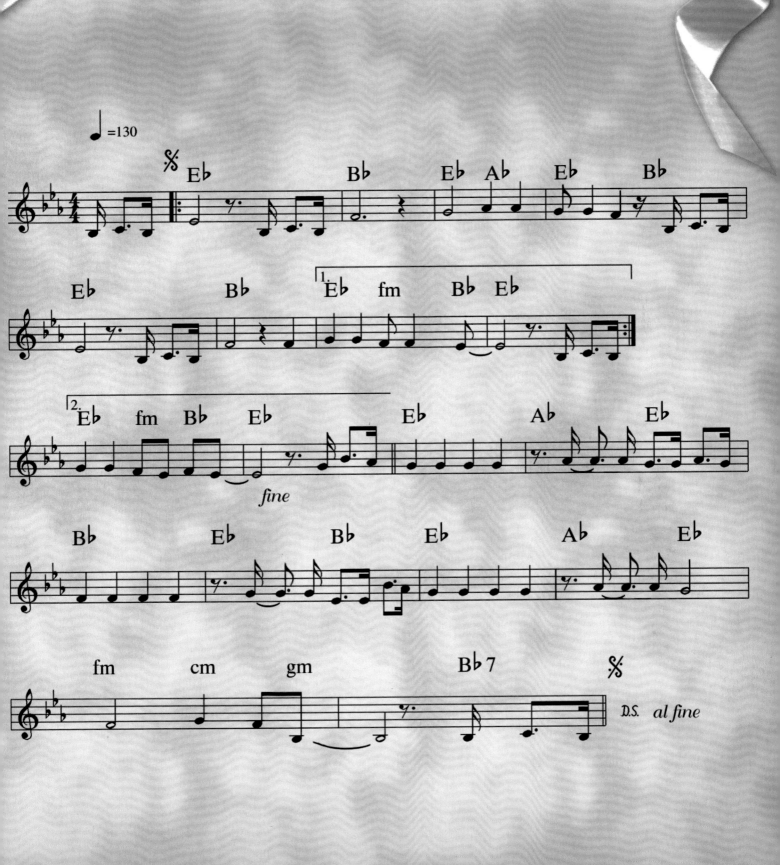

Thank G-d

I have two hands,
Thank G-d two healthy hands.
And what can I do with them?
Give charity, one two three.
And what can I do with them?
Give charity, one two three.[1]

I have two feet,
Thank G-d two healthy feet.
And where can I run with them?
To do good deeds in rain and snow.
And where can I run with them?
To do good deeds in rain and snow.

I have two eyes.
Thank G-d two healthy eyes.
And what can I do with them?
Read the alef-beyz.
And what can I do with them?
Read the alef-beyz.

I have two ears.
Thank G-d two healthy ears.
And when I hear a blessing,
I say: Amen.
And when I hear a blessing,
I say: Amen.

[1]In Yiddish, the idiom for something happening fast is *eyns un tsvey* (one, two); in English, the same thing is 'one, two, three.'

ג-ט צו דאַנקען

אָיך האָב צוויי הענטעלער,
ג-ט צו דאַנקען צוויי געזונטע הענטעלער.
און וואָס קען אָיך טאָן מיט זיי?
געבן צדקה, איינס און צוויי.
און וואָס קען אָיך טאָן מיט זיי?
געבן צדקה, איינס און צוויי.

אָיך האָב צוויי פֿיסעלער,
ג-ט צו דאַנקען צוויי געזונטע פֿיסעלער.
און ווּ קען אָיך לויפֿן מיט זיי?
טאָן מיצוות אין רעגן און שניי.
און ווּ קען אָיך לויפֿן מיט זיי?
טאָן מיצוות אין רעגן און שניי.

אָיך האָב צוויי אייגעלער,
ג-ט צו דאַנקען צוויי געזונטע אייגעלער.
און וואָס קען אָיך טאָן מיט זיי?
לייענען אַלף-בית.
און וואָס קען אָיך טאָן מיט זיי?
לייענען אַלף בית.

אָיך האָב צוויי אוירערלער,
ג-ט צו דאַנקען צוויי געזונטע אוירערלער.
און ווען אָיך הער מיט זיי אַ ברכה
זאָג אָיך: אָמן.
און ווען אָיך הער מיט זיי אַ ברכה
זאָג אָיך: אָמן.

G-t Tsu Danken

Ikh hob tsvey hentelekh,
G-t tsu danken tsvey gezunte hentelekh,
Un vos ken ikh ton mit zey?
Gebn tsedoke, eyns un tsvey.
Un vos ken ikh ton mit zey?
Gebn tsedoke, eyns un tsvey.

Ikh hob tsvey fiselekh,
G-t tsu danken tsvey gezunte fiselekh,
Un vu ken ikh loyfn mit zey?
Ton mitsves in regn un shney.
Un vu ken ikh loyfn mit zey?
Ton mitsves in regn un shney.

Ikh hob tsvey eygelekh,
G-t tsu danken tsvey gezunte eygelekh,
Un vos ken ikh ton mit zey?
Leyenen alef-beyz.
Un vos ken ikh ton mit zey?
Leyenen alef beyz.

Ikh hob tsvey oyerlekh,
G-t tsu danken tsvey gezunte oyerlekh,
Un ven ikh her mit zey
A brokhe zog ikh omeyn.
Un ven ikh her mit zey
A brokhe zog ikh omeyn.

Thank G-d

HaShem is Here

HaShem is here.
HaShem is there.
HaShem is everywhere.

HaShem is here.
HaShem is there.
HaShem is everywhere.

Here, here.
There, there
Right, left, everywhere
Down below,
High above,
In a Jew's heart
And mind.

HaShem is here.
HaShem is there.
HaShem is everywhere.

השם איז דא

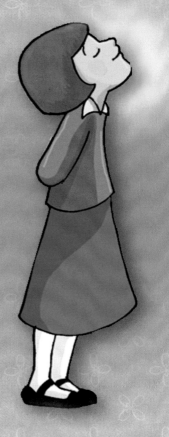

השם איז דאָ
השם איז דאָרט
השם איז אין יעדן אָרט

השם איז דאָ
השם איז דאָרט
השם איז אין יעדן אָרט

דאָ, דאָ
דאָרט, דאָרט
רעכטס, לינקס
ווי נאָר אַן אָרט
אין דער נידער
און זייער הויך
אין אַ ייִדנס האַרץ און מוח

השם איז דאָ
השם איז דאָרט
השם איז אין יעדן אָרט

HaShem iz Do

HaShem iz Do
HaShem iz Dort
HaShem iz in yeydn ort

HaShem iz Do
HaShem iz Dort
HaShem iz in yeydn ort

Do, Do
Dort, dort
Rekhts, links, vi nor an ort
In der nider
Un zeyer hoyekh
In a yidns harts un moyekh.

HaShem iz Do
HaShem iz Dort
HaShem iz in yeydn ort

HaShem is Here

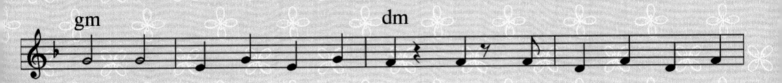

Rain

It's going to rain soon. 4x
Rain will soon fall. 2x

See, it's getting dark already.
It's getting dark already. 3x
It's already getting dark outside. 2x

See, the clouds are gathering.
The clouds are gathering. 3x
The clouds are gathering in the sky. 2x

The rain falls on the earth;
The earth soaks it up.
The roots drink from the earth,
And bring the rain into the tree.
The water goes up through the trunk
To the branches and the leaves
That are waiting for it.
And every leaf will not forget
To thank G-d in silent leaf-language
        for the food it gets.

So rain and fog are good.
One day it's wet
The second day there's an apple.

It's going to rain soon. 4x
Rain will soon fall. 2x

רעגן

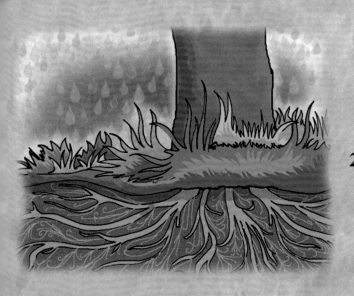

עס וועט באַלד רעגענען.   4X

עס וועט באַלד גיין אַ רעגן.   2X

זעסט, עס ווערט שוין פֿינצטער

עס ווערט שוין פֿינצטער   3X

עס ווערט שוין פֿינצטער אין דרויסן   2X

זעסט, די וואָלקנס זאַמלען זיך

די וואָלקנס זאַמלען זיך   3X

די וואָלקנס זאַמלען זיך אין הימל   2x

דער רעגן פֿאַלט אויף דער ערד.

די ערד, זי זאַפֿט אים אײַן.

די וואָרצלען טרינקען פֿון דער ערד,

און ברענגען דעם רעגן אין בוים אַרײַן.

דאָס וואַסער גייט דורכן שטאַם אַרויף

צו די צווײַגלעך און בלעטלער

וואָס וואַרטן דערויף.

און יעדעס בלעטל וועט ניט פֿאַרגעסן

אויף שטום בלעטלשפּראַך

דאַנקען ג־ט פֿאַרן עסן.

איז טאַקע גוט רעגן און נעפּל.

אײן טאָג איז נאַס.

דעם צווייטן ס'דאָ אַן עפּל.

עס וועט באַלד רעגענען.   4X

עס וועט באַלד גיין אַ רעגן.   2X

Regn

Es vet bald regenen   4x
Es vet bald geyn a regn. 2x

Zest, es vert shoyn fintster
Es vert shoyn fintster 3x
Es vert shoyn fintster in droysn 2x

Zest, di volkns zamlen zikh
Di volkns zamlen zikh 3x
Di volkns zamlen zikh in himl 2x

Der regn falt af der erd.
Di erd, zi zapt im ayn.
Di vortslen trinken fun der erd,
Un brengen dem regn in boym arayn.
Dos vaser geyt durkhn shtam aroyf
Tsu di tsvayglekh un bletlekh
Vos vartn deroyf.
Un yedes bletl vet nit fargesn
Af shtum bletl-shprakh danken G-t farn esn.

Is dokh take gut regn un nepl.
Eyn tog iz nas.
Dem tsveytn s'do an epl.

Es vet bald regenen. 4x
Es vet bald geyn a regn. 2x

Regn

The Wind is Blowing

The wind is blowing.   2X
The leaves are falling. 2X
The wind is blowing. 2X
The leaves are falling in the wind.

The wind is blowing. 2X
The flowers are dancing. 2X
The wind is blowing. 2X
The flowers are dancing in the wind.

The wind is blowing. 2X
The little birds are flying. 2X
The wind is blowing. 2X
The little birds soar in the wind.

G-d created a beautiful world,
And I like all of His creations. } 2X
    The little birds that fly,
    The flowers that bloom,
    The wind that cools,
    The dog that barks,
I like all of His creations.

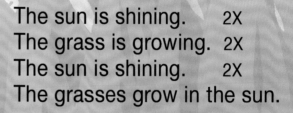

The sun is shining.   2X
The grass is growing. 2X
The sun is shining.   2X
The grasses grow in the sun.

The sun is shining.   2X
It warms up the nests. 2X
The sun is shining.   2X
The sun warms up the nests.

The sun is shining.   2X
The children are running. 2X
The sun is shining.   2X
The children run in the sun.

עס בלאָזט אַ ווינט

עס בלאָזט אַ ווינט.   2X
די בלעטעלעך פֿאַלן   2X
עס בלאָזט אַ ווינט.   2X
די בלעטעלעך פֿאַלן אין ווינט.

עס בלאָזט אַ ווינט.   2X
די בלימעלעך טאַנצן.   2X
עס בלאָזט אַ ווינט.   2X
די בלימעלעך טאַנצן אין ווינט.

עס בלאָזט אַ ווינט.   2X
די פֿייגעלעך פֿליִען.   2X
עס בלאָזט אַ ווינט.   2X
די פֿייגעלעך פֿליִען אין ווינט.

ג־ט האָט באַשאַפֿן אַ שיינע וועלט,   2X
און אַלע באַשעפֿענישן מיר געפֿעלן.

די פֿייגלער וואָס פֿליִען,
די בלימעלעך וואָס בליִען,
דער ווינט וואָס קילט,
דער הונט וואָס בילט.
אַלע באַשעפֿענישן מיר געפֿעלן.

עס שײַנט די זון.   2X
די גרעזעלעך וואַקסן.   2X
עס שײַנט די זון.   2X
די גרעזעלעך וואַקסן אין זון.

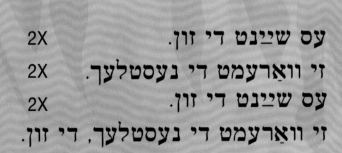

עס שײַנט די זון.   2X
זי וואַרעמט די נעסטלעך.   2X
עס שײַנט די זון.   2X
זי וואַרעמט די נעסטלעך, די זון.

עס שײַנט די זון.   2X
די קינדערלעך לויפֿן.   2X
עס שײַנט די זון.   2X
די קינדערלעך לויפֿן אין זון.

Es Blozt a Vint

Es blozt a vint   2X
Di bletelekh faln. 2X
Es blozt a vint. 2X
Di bletelekh faln in vint.

Es blozt a vint. 2X
Di blimelekh tantsn. 2X
Es blozt a vint. 2X
Di blimelekh tantsn in vint.

Es blozt a vint. 2X
Di feygelekh flien. 2X
Es blozt a vint. 2X
Di feygelekh flien in vint.

G-t hot bashafn a sheyne velt,
Un ale bashefeneshn mir gefeln. } 2X
   Di feyglekh vos flien,
   Di blimlekh vos blien,
   Der vint vos kilt,
   Der hunt vos bilt--
Un ale bashefeneshn mir gefeln.

Es shaynt di zun.   2X
Di grezelekh vaksn. 2X
Es shaynt di zun. 2X
Di grezelekh vaksn in zun.

Es shaynt di zun. 2X
Zi varemt di nestlekh. 2X
Es shaynt di zun. 2X
Zi varemt di nestlekh di zun.

Es shaynt di zun. 2X
Di kinderlekh loyfn. 2X
Es shaynt di zun. 2X
Di kinderlekh loyfn in zun.

The Wind is Blowing

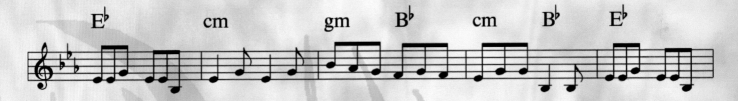

It Is Sabbath Quiet

It is Sabbath quiet.

What a good feeling.

The house is clean.

Charming.

Just as G-d wants it.

It is Sabbath fine.

The wine is ready.

The table is covered:

Ready.

Father will come home soon.

The Sabbath is a day of peace and rest.

After the *cholent*[1] one takes a nap.

One learns the Torah portion of the week;

One[2] learns from the *Tsene-Urene*,[3]

And the good angels listen.[4]

Because... it is Sabbath good.

Everything that one does

Is in the spirit of the Sabbath,

And it refreshes

A person and gives him strength.

[1]*Cholent* is a traditional dish eaten for lunch on the Sabbath. It is made with meat and potatoes. Some people add beans and barley and other ingredients. It cooks on a low flame from the beginning of the Sabbath on Friday night.

[2]Usually the women.

[3]The title of this book means 'Go and see.' It is an old collection of stories and explanations corresponding to the weekly Torah portion.

[4]It is said that both good and bad angels follow one home from the synagogue. If everything in the house is prepared for the Sabbath, the good angel says: May it be this way next Sabbath as well. And the bad angel is forced to agree.

ס'איז שא שבת שטיל

ס'איז שאַ שבת שטיל:

אַ גוט געפֿיל.

אין שטוב איז ריין,

מלא-חן,

פּונקט אַזוי ווי ג־ט וויל.

ס'איז שאַ שבת פֿײַן:

עס שטייט דער וויַין.

דער טיש איז פֿאַרשפּרייט,

צוגעגרייט

דער טאַטע קומט באַלד אַהיים.

שבת איז אַ טאָג פֿון מנוחה און רו.

נאָכן טשאָלנט לייגט מען זיך צו.

מע לערנט די סדרה

מע לייענט צאינה-וראינה,

און די גוטע מלאָכים הערן זיך צו.

וויַיל...ס'איז שאַ שבת גוט.

אַלץ וואָס מע טוט

איז שבתדיק און עס דערקוויקט

דעם מענטשן און גיט אים צו מוט.

S'iz Sha Shabes Shtil

S'iz sha Shabes shtil:
A gut gefil.
In shtub iz reyn,
Mole-kheyn.
Punkt azoy vi G-t vil.

S'iz sha Shabes fayn:
Es sheyt der vayn.
Der tish iz farshpreyt,
Tsugegreyt.
Der tate kumt bald aheym.

Shabes iz a tog fun menukhe un ru.
Nokhn tsholnt leygt men zikh tsu.
Me lernt di sedre,
Me leynt Tsene-Rene,
Un di gute malokhim hern zikh tsu.

Vayl...s'iz sha Shabes gut.
Alts vos me tut
Is Shabesdik
Un es derkvikt
Dem mentshn un git im tsu mut.

It Is Sabbath Quiet

Charity

Put another coin in
The little charity tin.
That's what a Jew does...
Gives charity, charity, charity.

And before Shabbos
    comes around
Put in another few pennies.
That's what a Jew does...
Gives charity, charity, charity.

Torah...if a Jew follows the Torah,
And he helps a poor man
    out with money,
G-d will supply him with
    what he himself lacks.

So, put another coin in
The little charity tin.
That's what a Jew does...
Gives charity, charity, charity.

צְדָקָה
charity

צדקה

לייג אַרײַן אַ מטבע

אינעם קלײנעם פּושקעלע.

אָט אַזוי טוט אַ ייִד,

גיט צדקה, צדקה, צדקה.

און איידער שבת קומט צו גיין

לייג אַרײַן אַ פּאָר גראָשן מער.

אָט אַזוי טוט אַ ייִד,

גיט צדקה, צדקה, צדקה.

תּורה, אַ ייִד היט אָפּ די תּורה,

און אַז ער העלפֿט אַן אָרעמאַן מיט געלט,

וועט אים ג־ט צוגעבן דאָס וואָס פֿעלט.

איז לייג אַרײַן אַ מטבע

אינעם קלײנעם פּושקעלע.

אָט אַזוי טוט אַ ייִד,

גיט צדקה, צדקה, צדקה.

Tsedoke

Leyg arayn a matbeye
Inem kleynem pushkele
Ot azoy tut a yid,
Git tsedoke, tsedoke, tsedoke.

Un eyder shabes kumt tsu geyn,
Leyg arayn a por groshn mer.
Ot azoy tut a yid,
Git tsedoke, tsedoke, tsedoke.

צְדָקָה

charity

Toyre, a yid hit op di toyre.
Un az er helft an oreman mit gelt,
Vet im G-t tsugebn dos vos felt.

Iz leyg arayn a matbeye
Inem kleynem pushkele
Ot azoy tut a yid,
Git tsedoke, tsedoke, tsedoke.

Charity

On The Occasion of My Birthday Today

On the occasion of my birthday today
All of my friends came
To give me blessings and to wish me success
On the occasion of my birthday today.
Mother baked a cake.
Father gave a talk.
He spoke words of Torah,
Praised our Creator,
On the good fortune of my birthday today.

Today I am three years old.
My grandmother says I'm almost
    ready to get married.
My locks have been cut,
But two lovely earlocks remain.

And what have I put on?
A new garment: *tsitsis*[1]
The four fine fringes
Remind me that I am a Jew,
And I wear them from today on,

Because I am three years old.
I want to thank all my good friends,
Who came to take part in
My joyous occasion today
To give me blessings and to wish me success
On the occasion of my birthday today.

[1]*Tsitsis* are also called a *tallis-kotn* 'a small tallis.' It is a four cornered garment with a fringe in each corner, donned by a young boy, when he reaches the age of three.

צו מײַן געבוירן־טאָג הײַנט

צו מײַן געבוירן־טאָג הײַנט
זײַנען געקומען אַלע גוטע־פֿרײַנד
געבן אַ ברכה און ווינטשן הצלחה
צו מײַן געבוירן־טאָג הײַנט.

די מאַמעיט געבאַקן אַ טאָרט.
דער טאַטע האָט אויך געגעבן אַ גוט וואָרט,
אַ וואָרט פֿון דער תּורה,
געלויבט אונדזער בורא,
וואָס מיט מזל יער איך זיך הײַנט.

הײַנט בין איך דרײַ יאָר אַלט.
די באָבע זאָגט כ׳וועּר אַ חתן־בחור באַלד:
די האָר אָפּגעשוירן,
די לאָקן פֿאַרלוירן,
נאָר צוויי שיינע פּאות בלײַבן.

און וואָס האָב איך אָנגעטאָן?
אַ נײַעם מלבוש: אַ טלית־קטן.
די פֿיר שיינע ציצית
דערמאָנען, דאָ אַ ייִד איז,
און איך טראָג זיי פֿון הײַנט אָן.

ווײַל הײַנט בין איך דרײַ יאָר אַלט,
וויל איך באַדאַנקען אַלע גוטע־פֿרײַנד,
וואָס זײַנען געקומען, אַן אָנטייל גענומען
אין מײַן גרויסער שמחה הײַנט.
געבן אַ ברכה און ווינטשן הצלחה
צו מײַן גרויסער שמחה הײַנט.

Tsu Mayn Geburtstog Haynt

Tsu mayn geboyrn-tog haynt
Zaynen gekumen ale gute-fraynd
Gebn a brokhe un vintshn hatslokhe
Tsu mayn geboyrn-tog haynt.

Di mame't gebakn a tort.
Der tate hot oykh gegebn a gut vort,
A vort fun der Toyre,
Geloybt undzer Boyre,
Vos mit mazl yer ikh zikh haynt.

Haynt bin ikh dray yor alt.
Di bobe zogt kh'ver a khosn-bokher bald:
Di hor opgeshoyrn,
Di lokn farloyrn,
Nor tsvey sheyne peyes blaybn.

Un vos hob ikh ongeton?
A nayem malbesh: a tales-koton.
Fir sheyne tsitses
Dermonen, sdo a Yid iz,
Un ikh trog zey fun haynt on.

Vayl haynt bin ikh dray yor alt,
Un ikh vil badanken ale gute-fraynd,
Vos zaynen gekumen,
An onteyl genumen
In mayn groyser simkhe haynt.
Gebn a brokhe un vintshn hatslokhe
Tsu mayn groyser simkhe haynt.

On The Occasion of My Birthday Today

Take Me to Kheyder

Take me to kheyder
To kheyder I want to go
Take me every day,
I want to study well.

There I will learn
How to be a good Jew.
Take me to kheyder today,
Please, dear mother.

There I will learn
About our great Torah.
I want to learn to pray
To praise our Creator.

There I will learn
About all our great holidays:
Passover, Purim, Shavuos,
And the Days of Awe.

We hear stories there
About our great rabbis.
How Jews must struggle
Against all of their enemies.

So take me to kheyder
To kheyder I want to go
Take me every day
I want to study well.

נעם מיך אין חדר

נעם מיך אין חדר,
אין חדר וויל איך גיין.
נעם מיך אַלע טאָג,
איך וויל זיך לערנען שיין.

איך וועל זיך דאָרט לערנען
צו זיַין אַ ייִד אַ גוטער.
נעם מיך היַינט אין חדר,
איך בעט דיך,   טיַיערע מוטער.

כ'וועל זיך דאָרט לערנען
פֿון אונזער גרויסע תּורה.
כ'וועל זיך לערנען דאַוונען
לויבן אונזער בורא.

איך וועל זיך דאָרט לערנען
פֿון אַלע די יום-טובֿים:
פּסח, פּורים, שבֿועות,
און די ימים-נוראָים.

מיר הערן דאָרט מעשׂיות
פֿון די גרויסע רבנים,
ווי ייִדן מוזן קעמפֿן
מיט אַלע זייערע שׂונאים.

איז נעם מיך אין חדר,
אין חדר וויל איך גיין.
נעם מיך אַלע טאָג,
איך וויל זיך לערנען שיין.

Nem Mikh in Kheyder

Nem mikh in kheyder,
In kheyder vil ikh geyn.
Nem mikh ale tog,
Ikh vil zikh lernen sheyn.

Ikh vel zikh dort lernen
Tsu zayn a yid a guter.
Nem mikh haynt in kheyder,
Ikh bet dikh, tayere muter.

Kh'vel zikh dort lernen
Fun undzer groyse Toyre.
Kh'vel zikh lernen davenen,
Loybn undzer Boyre.

Ikh vel zikh dort lernen
Fun ale di yontoyvim:
Peysekh, purim , shvues,
Un di yoymim-neroyim.

Mir hern dort mayses
Fun di groyse rabonim,
Vi yidn muzn kemfn
Mit ale zeyere sonim.

Iz nem mikh in kheyder,
In kheyder vil ikh geyn.
Nem mikh ale tog,
Ikh vil zikh lernen sheyn.

Take Me to Kheyder

Why Does the Child Cry?

Why is the little girl crying?
Why does the child cry?
Did you hurt your little nail?
Mommy will give it a kiss now.

One really feels better when one has a cry,
And things feel better on mommy's lap.
Mommy will give you a hug,
And look at the boo-boo.
And one-two-three...like magic;
One's eyes are dry.

Why is the little boy crying?
Why does the child cry?
Did you bite your little tongue?
Mommy will give you a kiss now.

One really feels better when one has a cr
And things feel better on mommy's lap.
Mommy will give you a hug,
And look at the boo-boo.
And one-two-three...like magic;
One's eyes are dry.

פֿאַר וואָס זשע וויינט דאָס קינד?

פֿאַר וואָס זשע וויינט דאָס מיידעלע?

פֿאַר וואָס זשע וויינט דאָס קינד?

צי טוט דיר ווי אין נעגעלע?

גיט די מאַמע אַ קוש אַצינד.

מע פֿילט זיך טאַקע בעסער ווען מע וויינט זיך אויס,

און ס'ווערט גיכער בעסער אויף דער מאַמעס שויס.

די מאַמע וועט דיך אַרומנעמען,

און דעם ווייטיק באַקוקן,

און איינס און צוויי ווי כּישוף טאָן

ווערן די אויגן טרוקן.

פֿאַר וואָס זשע וויינט דאָס ייִנגעלע?

פֿאַר וואָס זשע וויינט דאָס קינד?

צי האָסטו זיך צעביסן דאָס צינגעלע?

גיט די מאַמע אַ קוש אַצינד.

מע פֿילט זיך טאַקע בעסער ווען מע וויינט זיך אויס,

און ס'ווערט גיכער בעסער אויף דער מאַמעס שויס.

די מאַמע וועט דיך אַרומנעמען,

און דעם ווייטיק באַקוקן,

און איינס און צוויי ווי כּישוף טאָן

ווערן די אויגן טרוקן.

Far Vos Veynt Dos Kind?

Far vos zhe veynt dos meydele?
Far vos zhe veynt dos kind?
Tsi tut dir vey in negele?
Git di mame a kush atsind.

Me filt zikh take beser ven me veynt zikh oys,
Un s'vert gikher beser af der mames shoys.
Di mame vet dikh arumnemen,
Un dem veytik bakukn,
Un eyns un tsvey...vi kishef ton,
Vern di oygn trukn.

Far vos zhe veynt dos yingele?
Far vos zhe veynt dos kind?
Tsi host zikh tsebisn dos tsingele?
Git di mame a kush atsind.

Me filt zikh take beser ven me veynt zikh oys,
Un s'vert gikher beser af der mames shoys.
Di mame vet dikh arumnemen,
Un dem veytik bakukn,
Un eyns un tsvey...vi kishef ton,
Vern di oygn trukn.

Why Does the Child Cry?

I am a Good Boy

I can sing, sing, sing,
I can dance around, and I can jump,
But I am a good boy.
All father has to do is call,
And I become quiet and listen,
Because one should listen to one's father!

Refrain

Honoring one's father and mother
Is a very good thing,
And it's written in the Torah:
That if you obey your parents,
You will live longer,
And you are doing yourself a favor.

I can play, play, play,
On the chairs, on the floors,
But I am a good girl.
When mother says the word,
I put everything in its place,
Because one should listen
    to one's mother.

Refrain

איך בין אַ ייִנגעלע אַ גוטער

איך קען זינגען, זינגען, זינגען,

איך קען טאַנצן, איך קען שפרינגען,

אָבער כ'בין אַ ייִנגעלע אַ גוטער.

ווען דער טאַטע טוט אַ רוף,

ווער איך שטיל און הער זיך צו,

ווײַל מע דאַרף פאָלגן אַ פאָטער!

רעפרען:

כבוד אָבֿ ואם

איז דאָך זייער שיין

און עס שטייט געשריבן אין דער תורה:

ווען דו פאָלגסט די עלטערן

וועסט זיך די יאָרן פאַרלענגערן

און דו טוסט זיך אַליין אַ טובה.

איך קען זיך שפילן, שפילן, שפילן

אויף די בענקלער, אויף די דילן,

אָבער כ'בין אַ מיידעלע אַ גוטע.

ווען די מאַמע זאָגט אַ וואָרט

לייג איך אַלצדינג אויפֿן אָרט,

ווײַל מע דאַרף פאָלגן אַ מוטער!

רעפרען:

Ikh bin a Yingele a Guter

Ikh ken zingen, zingen, zingen,
Ikh ken tantsn, ikh ken shpringen,
Ober kh'bin a yingele a guter
Ven der tate tut a ruf,
Ver ikh shtil un her zikh tsu,
Vayl me darf folgn a foter!

Refren:

Kibud av ve eym
Iz dokh zeyer sheyn
Un es shteyt geshribn in der Toyre:
Ven du folgst di eltern,
Vest zikh di yorn farlengern
Un du tust zikh aleyn a toyve.

Ikh ken zikh shpiln, shpiln, shpiln,
Af di benklekh, af di diln,
Ober kh'bin a meydele a gute.
Ven di mame zogt a vort,
Leyg ikh altsding afn ort,
Vayl me darf folgn a muter!

Refren:

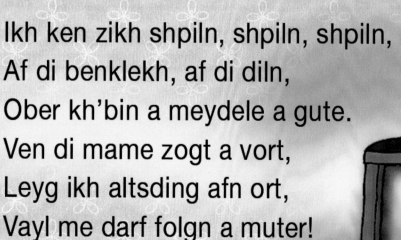

I am a Good Boy